If You Cold See Laughter

MANDY COE is an award-winning poet and artist. She has published six books including three collections of poetry for adults and one for children. Her work has been featured on BBC television and radio and she reads at literature events across the UK.

As a freelance writer, Mandy works with community groups and inner-city schools. Her guide to the work of writers in schools *Our thoughts are bees* (co-written with Jean Sprackland) was described by Andrew Motion as 'inspiring, enlightening and far-reaching'.

Mandy Coe's first collection *Pinning the Tail on the Donkey* was shortlisted for the Aldeburgh First Collection Prize. Her poetry for children is anthologised by Macmillan, Oxford University Press and Bloomsbury. Mandy is a Hawthornden Fellow.

Also by Mandy Coe

POETRY FOR ADULTS
Pinning the Tail on the Donkey (Spike 2000)
The Weight of Cows (Shoestring Press 2004)
Clay (Shoestring Press 2009)

NON-FICTION
Our thoughts are bees: Writers Working with Schools (Wordplay Press 2005)

GRAPHIC NOVEL
Red Shoes (Good Stuff Press 1997)

MANDY COE

If You Could See Laughter

Illustrated by Mandy Coe

CHILDREN'S POETRY LIBRARY
No. 6

SALT

LONDON

PUBLISHED BY SALT PUBLISHING
Dutch House, 307-308 High Holborn,
London WC1V 7LL United Kingdom

© Mandy Coe, 2010
Illustrations © Mandy Coe

The right of Mandy Coe to be identified as the
editor of this work has been asserted by her in accordance
with Section 77 of the Copyright, Designs and Patents Act 1988.

First published 2010

Printed in the UK by the MPG Books Group

Typeset in Oneleigh 11 / 14

ISBN 978 1 84471 487 2 paperback

1 3 5 7 9 8 6 4 2

*'Day by day I float my paper boats one by one
down the running stream.
In big black letters I write my name on them and the name
of the village where I live.'*
—RABINDRANATH TAGORE

CONTENTS

ACKNOWLEDGEMENTS

Thanks to the editors of the following anthologies in which these poems first appeared: 'Assembly' in *The Works 6*, Macmillan; 'Bottling it Up' in *Here Come the Heebie Jeebies*, Hodder Wayland; 'Busy Feet' in *The Oxford Reading Tree*, Oxford University Press; 'Can-can' in *Hot Heads, Warm Hearts, Cold Streets*, Stanley Thornes; 'Catch Words' in *Playing With Words*, Pelican; 'How the Light', 'Me & You', 'Thank You', 'The Head's First Name', 'The Sunshine of Susan Browne' and 'When Ms Smith' in *Read Me At School*, Macmillan; 'Marsh Sprite' and 'Wish' in *Fairy Poems*, Macmillan; 'Schoolday's End' in *Spooky Schools*, Macmillan; 'Sensing Mother' in *Sensational*, Bloomsbury; 'The Girl Who Lit the First Fire' in *Wicked*, Bloomsbury; 'Soft as the Blanket' in *Michael Rosen's A–Z: The Best Children's Poetry from Agard to Zephaniah*, Puffin.

'The Cloud That Fell' was commissioned by *Can I have a Word*, the Barbican.

ADVICE FOR . . .

PONIES

let the pictures flow
what do you see?
taste every sound
      neat?
      tidy?
      no
look at apples
without saying apple
be brave
thoughts can interrupt thinking
run fast
learn to stand still

POETS

dream of a land without fences
never show anyone how high you can really jump
accept kindness softly
between the stars and each sweet blade of grass
lie secrets that sound like grasshoppers
let frost make your breath white
know that you are the creator of all rhythms found
      between stillness
and the rare moments you run so fast
you no longer touch the ground

SEASHELL

Have you seen it? A pink-tinted
coil of air . . . about
so big?

At one end can be heard
the open roar of sea, the other
narrows to silence and infinity.
In between is nothing,

shaped like a ringlet
or honeysuckle twine, and
(before the orange grip
of oyster-catcher's beak)
it was the exact shape of me.

Have you seen that coil of air
where my soft self should be?

FELT FUNNY ALL DAY

There was a man
who left his house in such a rush
he shut the front door on his shadow.

The shadow knocked, the shadow called
though its knuckles made no noise
and its voice stirred no air.

The man walked for a while
but his footsteps sounded loud.
He sat on a bench

but the bench felt hard.
He read his newspaper,
but the words seemed to dance.

The man scratched his head
wondering what
he had forgotten.

At home the shadow
zigzagged itself on the stairs,
flattened itself against the window.

In the end it hung itself on the hat-stand,
neat as an ironed shirt. *I've felt funny all day,*
said the man as he let himself in.

He hung up his hat, tapped his chest
with his fist and burped:
must have been indigestion.

'FLOWERS GO TO SCHOOL UNDERGROUND'

RABINDRANATH TAGORE

Flowers beneath snow,
inside the earth,
within the seed.

Flowers in honeycomb,
girls' names,
the scented foam of soap.

Flowers in the thread,
a swift needle's tip,
the dancing swirl of skirt.

Flowers in the paint,
the bristles of the brush,
hummingbird dreams.

Flowers in fireworks,
deep in flowerpots, flowers
humming to the bees.

MOORHEN

She is the clown of all waterfowl,
stubby and black,
plastic yellow feet, bright red nose.
The eggs — her treasures — are carefully
raised from dog-brown water
on a flimsy throne of twigs.

Her partner honks a warning
at reeds, rats, ripples, sky.
Through park railings
a toddler drops a fistful of white bread.

The eggs are alive with tiny vibrations.
Like nightfall, black feathers
settle and still them.

RAW

We always tiptoe up to rhubarb
and braving the prick of leaves,
kneel in muck
bending the angled stem
until the glassy *snap*.

Something draws us to it,
the sly creak of its shine,
the rawness
that strips spit, making our teeth
feel coated and sharp.

We push out tongues
in gargoyle astonishment,
let half-chewed dollops drop
between our feet. How could the sweet
pink of rhubarb and custard come from this?

Behind splintered sheds
where old men tip rumbling wheelbarrows,
we prepare to bite into onion.

RECIPE FOR GOOD NEWS

I want to make news
the way a baker bakes a cake,
because the news I'd bake
won't make grandma's smile
turn upside-down
while she sighs at the radio:
What's the world coming to?

I want to make news
the way a baker bakes a cake,
because the news I'd bake
won't make mum bang shirts with the iron
while shouting at the telly:
Tell the truth for once why don't you!

I want to make news
the way a baker bakes a cake,
because the news I'd make
will have everyone cheering
for dark red cherries and chocolate icing.

My news will be so good
we'll gather round to share it,
lick the crumbs off our fingers.

IF YOU COULD SEE LAUGHTER

Hey, it is blue! No, surely red
— the colour of each breath
pumped out by the joy of running
or the jumpstart of a joke.

Tickle-breath is long and spiral.
Pink
I think.

If you could see laughter
it would look like balloons,
the sort magicians knot in squeaky twists.
Laugh a giraffe, guffaw a poodle.

A belly-laugh creates balloons that float,
at the pantomime, the air of the theatre
jostles with colour.
See this baby reaching for your smile?
A yellow hiccup of laughter pops out,
bobs above us for days.

We could rise off the ground with laughter,
tie strings on it and sail around the world.

TOO YOUNG TO KNOW

In town the shutters stay closed.
We sleep with our clothes on.
The hall is full of bags.
Everyone goes quiet
when an aeroplane passes.

Uncle's shop is empty.
No warm smells of seedcake,
no queuing women to ruffle my hair.

From my bed I hear my family talking,
but when I dare to ask, when I dare
to touch my mother's hand and ask,
she says I am too young to understand.

Even the dog senses something,
creeping under the table, tail held low.
I hug his neck and whisper into his soft ear,
What is to happen? He licks my cheek.

ONE PAIR A YEAR

And as they wear out
you tie string around the toes
as if to silence a flapping mouth.
Line them with paper: headlines, local news.

You try to walk even, walk light.
Hammering nails into heels
you click and clack.
Every day you slip them off to save them,
side by side on the porch step,
in the shadow of a chair.
All dancing is done with bare feet.

Stones bruise, jute cuts,
it hurts you — or wears out the shoes.
Your decision, each journey,
each time you rise from chair or bed.
You walk to work, shoes bumping your chest,
the laces biting the back of your neck.

THANK YOU

Danke, merci, gracias
for the heat of the sun,
the kindness of teaching,
the smell of fresh bread.

Diolch, nkosi, shur-nur-ah-gah-lem
for the sound of sand,
children singing,
the book and the pen.

Dhannyabad, blagodaria, hvala
for the blue of small flowers,
the bobbing seal's head,
the taste of clean water.

Shukran gazillan, yakoke, nandi
for the stripe of the zebra,
the song of the chaffinch,
the gentleness of snails.

Mh goi, abarka, mille grazie
for the length of time,
the loveliness of eyelashes,
the arc of the ball.

Dziekuje, bhala hove, shakkran
for the excitement of falling,
the stillness of night,
my heart beating, thank you.

FROG

The frog has neatly folded legs.
Jaw of bulldog,
pond-skinned, up-eyed. This frog
has a double chin that throbs:
frog, he sings, *frog*.

Now he fans his toes and leaps
into a ring of ripples.
He grew himself, this frog,
from a black dot
in a see-through blob.

He measures time
in tongue-lengths and hops,
this damsel fly: gone!
Only a blink-of-an-eye gulp revealing
what occurs between verses of his song.

ROW FLOW BLOW
For Matt Simpson

an old man in a boat asked me
asked me how to go
I know, I said, I know
row, you've got to row
row, flow, blow
row, flow, blow

the tides of the sea they asked me
asked me how to go
I know, I said, I know
flow, you've got to flow
row, flow, blow
row, flow, blow

The wind behind the sails asked me
asked me how to go
I know, I said, I know
blow, you've got to blow
row, flow, blow
row, flow, blow

SENSING MOTHER

Dad keeps Mum's favourite dress
deep in the bottom of the ottoman.
Sometimes, when he is at work
I stand listening to the tick of the clock
then go upstairs.

And propping up the squeaky wooden lid,
I dig through layers
of rough, winter blankets
feeling for that touch of silk.
The blue whisper of it, cool
against my cheek.

Other times, the school-test times,
and dad-gets-home-too-late
to-say-goodnight times —
I wrap the arms of the dress around me,
breathing in a smell, faint as dried flowers.

I remember how she twirled around
— like a swirl of sky.

When I am old enough I will wear it.
Pulling up the white zip,
I'll laugh and spin,
calling out to *my* daughter:
How do I look?

SUN LOVES MOON

Monday, small ads:
    Hey Moonie-La, meet me at dawn S x

Tuesday, text:
    c u l8r :-) ?

Wednesday, diary extract:
    I will never EVER call her again.

Thursday, voicemail:
    Hi M, it's me. Did you get the flowers?
    Sorry about the chocolates,
    I put them in my pocket and they got . . . runny.
    Listen — is there any chance of us meeting?
    Please, *please* call me.

Friday, graffiti:
    Sun ♥ Moon

Saturday, singing telegram:
Greetings Miss, I love your face.
Please stop this eternal chase.
Will you be mine and let me shine?
My palest, roundest, Valentine.

Sunday, invitation:
Engagement party! Bring a friend. RSVP

WHAT LIVES DOWN THE PLAYGROUND DRAIN

You woke me. Again!
Leaning over my dark edge
you call down: *Halloo! Halloo!*

Up through the iron grating I see you
silhouetted against a square of sky.
Roots poke down gossip

of breeze and sunshine.
Worms bring tales of singing birds,
children's games.

Day after hollow day I echo
as you rain down pebbles, the splash
of marbles and pennies.

Even when the kindness of night
offers sleep,
your stories ripple my skin.

THE SUNSHINE
OF SUSAN BROWNE

Heat melts, makes liquid bubble.
Ice burns your skin, hurts your teeth.
Susan Browne understands these things.
She counts stars — gives new ones names.

Today she learned about the footprints
of dinosaurs. Last week she discovered
the heart of a flower looks like a cathedral.
She measures water in a beaker,
she weighs out sand and smiles.

Through the microscope
ants are giants; feathers are forests;
sugar is snow. And inside Susan Browne
swirls a galaxy of questions, curiosity
making her shine like a sun.

THE HEAD'S FIRST NAME

It just slipped past his young wife's lips
as she stood in a yellow dress, calling
and waggling her fingers
over the roof of her car.
And suddenly

we saw him
not as Sir,
with his dark suit and shiny briefcase.
Not as Mr stand-to-attention McGregor,
but as Frederick,
Fred,
Freddie.

And without taking his eyes off his shoes
he elbowed through
fifty hand-over-mouth grins,
the tips of his ears
glowing red.

WHEN MS SMITH SLAMMED THE CLASSROOM DOOR

It frightened up a flock of pigeons on the back field.
It made the Yorkshire puddings
collapse with a sigh.

It didn't crack ceilings.
It didn't make wars.
It didn't make the summer holidays any shorter.

But it did play on our minds
over and over again.

SUMMER SONG

Picnic beneath a singing sky
bright with blue and sun.
Far from the dash and rush of it all,
the tick-tock day — the yawn.

Paddle in singing water
the silver tickle of fish.
Far from the roar of motorways,
the growl of the 82 bus.

Cuddle up under singing stars,
the bat's calls, high and thin.
Far from clicking keyboards,
the blue computer screen.

Breathe the singing air my love,
breathe it out and breathe it in.
Tomorrow we'll get up early
— do all of this again.

FIZZ

When you laugh you bubble.
If you were food you would be sherbet,
a vanilla ice-cream float.
No glass is tall enough to hold you, no stripy straw
long enough to capture the froth.

When you jump you sparkle.
If you were rain you would be skyful,
drumming umbrellas,
rattling drainpipes. Rivers race,
but you beat them.

When you smile you glow.
If you were a torch
the man in the moon would yell,
turn out that light!
You banish shadow.

Champagne corks, summer rain, fireworks . . .
the fizz of you beats them all.

BED OF GLASS

Snail asleep on my windowpane,
brittle crust sealing out the world.
From inside I watch
your grey-fisted sleep,
rust-tinted, light shining
through your fragile shell.

I raise a finger, but don't tap.
It is so trusting,
this sharing of your secret life.

Imagine a mattress of glass,
my flattened face eyeing its way
blindly through dreams.

OPPOSITES

How the light
creates columns of dust in the classroom
slants through windows in the school hall
fires the trees with green flame
spills across the whiteboard
polishes the goldfish
makes us blink in the playground
lengthens our shadows by home-time

How the dark
pools under hanging coats and bags
is caught in empty wellingtons
gathers in the storeroom cupboard
hides behind hands as we count to ten
sleeps inside pencils
falls like curtains in the winter
fills the school when we've all gone home

THE GIFT

"Plucking the grass to see where sits the wind ..."

—SHAKESPEARE

Banged your door last week,
made the cat
leap off your lap.

Took your aunt's hat — the silk one,
threw it like a Frisbee,
then dropped it in the dirt.

You know the scattered leaves
your father heaped so carefully?
I did that.

I also stole your kite,
tore your tent,
kept you awake all night.

But today I bring you the sun.
I chased away the clouds!
Listen

to the music of the forest.
Do you see me
dancing with the trees?

ASSEMBLY

Raindrops run
down windowpanes,
leap into puddles. Streams bounce
across rocks, rush to the lakes.
The sea sucks in its breath,
breathes out . . .
and the world is blue with water.

Here we are, a river of us
spilling down corridors,
flowing into the hall,
skidding to a stop.
Teachers walk a sea's edge
of crossed legs, shifting feet,
giggles, a foam of skirts.

At the clock-ticking end
we will flow again.
Pouring round adults as if
they are the barnacled posts of a pier,
the bones of a wrecked ship.

SCHOOLDAY'S END

When I was built
children walked for miles,
called by my iron bell.
No cars, electric light or felt pens.
Just hurrying feet, the hiss of gaslight
and the squeal of chalk on slate.

They say that I am haunted now.
My attic creaks, twisted
black gates bang in the wind.
A shadow-game flickers across the yard.
These days, the children hurry past me
to the new school. I see them
carrying their toys and picture-books,
lunch-boxes and football boots.
The new school is warm and full of music,
its windows, bright with cut-out shapes.
Mine are dark and broken.

This long night is the last.
Moonlight spills down my slate roof.
I wish my bell could ring out again:
Come to me children! Run! Run!
Tomorrow the bulldozers come.

ELEMENTAL RULES

Ice
do let blades slide across your back
form a new country between sky and lake
creak and crack
tinkle in a cocktail glass

don't let the sun make you sweat
sting the polar bear's paws
let blue icecaps become blue lakes
topple Aunt Maureen on the back step

Fire
do create six flickering flames on this cake
make beans bubble, chapattis brown
roll and boil across the face of the sun
light circles of sing-song under the stars

don't race faster than wind across the prairies
go to sleep in damp winter hearths
exhale black breath in the fire-fighter's eye
bubble up red from the heart of the earth

Air
do swoosh in and out of elephants' lungs
lift the wings of the aeroplane
ripple lochs and fill out white sails
carry the vibrations of a lover's song

don't come up burping in the middle of a speech
bubble out the lilo so we sink in the pool
leave the room so all of us yawn
make us scream escaping the balloon

OFFENDED CAT

She turns her back,
busies herself with washing.
One ear flicks toward you, but

she has scratched you off
her purring-list. Watch her
tail-tip twitch. It speaks.

Do not be fooled
by lack of hiss.
If she were flash-eyed,

claws unsheathed, this
would be less serious.
As it is (until she decides

to grant you forgiveness)
you no longer exist.

QUEEN OF THE HIVE

Bill, butter my bread,
Zoë, wipe my lips.
Shirley! Shoelaces.
Tina! Silk scarf please.

The phone rings, the doorbell chimes.
Curtains open and close.
I don't lift a finger;
no one bothers me with these things.

My workers buzz around, it's exhausting
keeping them in line.
Shirley, droop my shoulders,
Barry — gently now — shake my head.

I am their queen, their world,
flowers, pollen, gold . . . all mine.
Susan, raise my right eyebrow,
now shape my mouth into a sad smile.

A smile, not a grin you stupid girl!
Without me they would have nothing,
a paper-thin castle
that could blow away on the wind.

THE STRAWBERRY-YOGHURT SMELL OF WORDS

Once we made a telephone,
twine stretched tight
between two yoghurt pots.
"Hello?   Hello?"
Communication!
You spoke.
I heard.

Now
it's a one-person game:
a thumb-dance of text,
beep of inbox. But don't you miss
that tug on the string?
The strawberry yoghurt
smell of words?

SWIMMING ON
CHRISTMAS DAY

The keys were in an envelope under the tree,
Uncle Sal held it jingling by the corner
and with the other hand,
tapped the side of his nose.
A friend of a friend, he said.

So there we were
floating on our backs. No one else, just us.
Uncle Sal wearing trunks and a Rudolf nose.
It's kind of like a cathedral, he said.
If we sing a few hymns
no one will ever know you missed church.

And so we sang: We Three Kings
and Little Town of Bethlehem.
Uncle Sal sang one underwater
and I guessed from the bubbles
. . . Silent Night.

We swam in circles, not lines.
We swam making no noise at all.
The sun shone through the glass roof
and made rainbows in our eyelashes.

When we got out
Uncle Sal turned on the hot drinks machine.
It jumped and rattled like his car.
The Bovril burned our fingers through the plastic cups.
As good as any Christmas dinner! Uncle Sal said.
We walked home smelling of chlorine.

LIGHTHOUSE

I will outshine the stars.
At my feet waves crash
while I spread bright arms and dance.

The moon is jealous, her buttery face
heavy with sulking. Only I can
flash and point, catching
the eye of fishermen,
the captain and sleepy cabin-boy.

Wake up!
Sharp rocks bite, the moon is hauling in
her angry tides. Every night,
whiter than the albatross
my light saves lives.

BEING THE BADDIE
Reasons to forgive us

(I)

I live in darkness.
Everyone who visits arrives with a sword.
I loved a man . . . he turned into stone.
When I reach out at night
there's no hand to hold.
The snakes keep me company
— but the hissing, oh the hissing.

(II)

Swirling the cloak gives me confidence.
The tooth fairy visited once
(she never came again). The sun
brings me out in a rash. I have an allergy
to all food . . . but one. Can I help it
if you leave your windows open at night?

(III)

What a telltale she was, tiptoeing about
on those teeny tiny feet.
Ugly? Come here and say that!
Ok, so mother buys us hideous dresses
— she can't accept that we hate princes,
and that beauty is only skin deep.

(IV)

You cut down our forest,
put my brother's skin around your shoulders
and wore it to the opera.
Our songs are as old as the mountains.
We are not big, nor bad, but all of us wonder
if you taste better than you look.

BOTTLING IT UP

If you bottle up
your worries and fears,
bottle them up for years
and years, they'll slowly
fill you to the top
until one day you'll just go . . .

POP!

And every single scary feeling
will be splattered across
the kitchen ceiling.
So save the mess,
admit you're scared.
Worries get smaller
when they are shared.

FROM THE MOUTHS OF BABES

Tongue speaks of some
speaks of none
a young tongue can tell no wrong.

Tongue pokes fun
sticks out too long
a young tongue can tell no wrong.

Any poem, any song
tongue sings along
a young tongue can tell no wrong.

Hold it, soap it
— can't be undone
a young tongue can tell no wrong.

BUSY FEET

Along the busy pavement
lots of busy feet.
Stand and look and listen
then cross the busy street.
Popping in the busy shop
to buy some food to eat.
Hopping on the busy bus
and wobbling to a seat.
Along the busy pavement,
along the busy street,
hopping, shopping,
never stopping,
busy, busy feet.

IN MY NAME
(*MANDY*)

In my name are mountains,
blue and white and high.
My name holds a thousand
miles of rock and sky.

In my name are valleys
climbed by Ma and Man
with a forked-top walking stick,
ready to hold a thumb.

In my name is a yacht's sail,
the sound of the river Dee.
In my name is a world,
in my name is me.

MARSH-SPRITE

It's not about the inky night
and the miles of bubbling marsh,
it's this skip of a heartbeat
when you glimpse a small blue light
and decide whether to lay down your foot
a little to the left,
or a little to the right.

They say this hungry mud
will swallow a horse before it takes fright,
so you'll trust the stars,
the whisper of reeds — anything
even this little blue light.

Lift one foot and start
the long journey home.
Please little light
be true.
Please be true
little light.

SOFT AS THE BLANKET

I can touch a coin and tell you
if it's heads or if it's tails.
I can taste a loaf of bread
and swear the baker wore blue shoes.
  Say a daft thing and make me grin,
  I'm as soft as the blanket
  you wrapped me in.

One silver raindrop on my tongue
and I feel the height of its fall.
If I brush a feather along my wrist
I know the miles it flew.
  Say a daft thing and make me grin,
  I'm as soft as the blanket
  you wrapped me in.

If I touch my lips to a stem of grass
I know what hour it was cut.
If I smell a yellow pencil
I'll tell you the last word it wrote.
  Say a daft thing and make me grin,
  I'm as soft as the blanket
  you wrapped me in.

I can taste in a grain of salt
the whale-songs of the sea.
If I touch your sleepy head I know
the colour of your dreams.
    Say a daft thing and make me grin,
    I'm as soft as the blanket
    you wrapped me in.

CATCH WORDS

Throw me a word
and we'll play **catch**
Throw me itch
and I'll throw you . . . ?

Throw me red
and I'll throw you **hot**
Throw me tea
and I'll throw you . . . ?

Throw me dust
and I'll throw you **bin**
Throw me a banana
and I'll throw you . . . ?

Throw me bangers
and I'll throw you **mash**
And if you drop a word or two
it'll all go . . . !

scratch, pot, skin, crash!

UPON ONCE

Once Upon A Time
there was you, there was the world,
and you moved about this world
with magic in your bones.

A Once Upon Time
you opened your arms
and climbed through air
ribbons of sunlight tangling in your hair.
You slid up a rainbow,
the green staining your hands.

Upon A Once Time
you lived under the sea
and walking between seaweed trees
bubbles of thought rose from your head
as if it were a sponge
squeezed by the fist of an idea.

Time A Once Upon
you packed a suitcase
and lived in a dream for a week.
You visited a theatre of ice,
a castle of clouds, you sent postcards
people had to be asleep to receive.

A Once Upon Time
there was you, there was the world,
and you moved about this world
with magic in your bones.

BUTTERCUP

Buttercups gleam, bright butter gold,
buttercup, buttercup, buttercup-cup.

Buttercups, tall, rambling wild,
buttercup, buttercup, buttercup-cup.

Butterflies and daisies dancing in the meadow,
buttercup, buttercup, buttercup-cup.

Bare legs tickled by green and yellow,
buttercup, buttercup, buttercup-cup.

Buttercups singing the summertime tune,
buttercup, buttercup, buttercup-cup.

Buttercups close at the rise of the moon,
buttercup, buttercup, buttercup-cup.

QUESTIONS FOR A DAD

Can you sleep when it's dark Dad?
Do monsters march round in your head?
Does your heart thump when you hear a creak?
Do you have to check under the bed?

Are you embarrassed when you're with girls Dad?
Do they giggle when you walk by?
Don't you hate it when girls say they love you?
Does it make you all red-faced and shy?

I miss you when you're at work Dad,
do you sometimes think of me too?
How much money do you make Dad?
And what is it you actually do?

Is it hard being a man Dad?
Is it prickly having a beard?
Do you feel just like me — only bigger?
Is being a dad really weird?

MY MA

My Ma's got hairy legs, her eyes
are bright, her ears stick out,
she runs down hills. My Ma
loves to shout, she loves to shout.

My Ma's breath is hot, her teeth
are yellow, she grinds them
at night. Wolves hide when Ma grins.
My Ma can fight, she can fight.

My Ma hugs trees, her arms
squeeze them tight, her brown hair
gleams. My Ma dreams, my Ma
dreams of honey every night.

BEING HUMAN

Can't find my fins.
I swim, fish swim,
here's me swimming . . .
So where are my fins?

Can't find my snout.
I dig, pigs dig,
here's me digging . . .
So where is my snout?

Can't find my tail.
I howl, wolves howl,
here's me howling . . .
So where is my tail?

Can't find my shell.
I crawl, crabs crawl,
here's me crawling . . .
So where is my shell?

Can't find my wings.
I sing, birds sing,
here's me singing . . .
So where are my wings?

Can find my arms and legs,
ears and eyes and skin.
Oh and a million thoughts and pictures . . .
So where is my paper and pen?

WISH

As a child she wanted to fly.
She wished for friends
who were birds and flowers.
She wished she wore a silver frock.

She wished she could speak
with a magic tongue.
She wished so hard,
she wished so hard.

Now she works in the pasty shop,
wears an apron and hairnet cap.
She speaks the language
of mam and dad, and at the end
of the day her feet are tired.

But each time the full moon shines
she carries her baby to the stars,
sings to him in the language of flowers.
He reaches to touch her silver wings.

THE GIRL WHO DISCOVERED FIRE

From her habit of chipping at flint
the red flower blossomed.
Magical at first, but
those who reached to touch it
ran howling into the bushes,
so she'd pause in her tap-tapping
to shrug an apology
as they crashed about in the dark.

No one talked about it directly.
No one knew the word for fire.
There was no back-slapping
or thanking the gods for a force
that brought the shine of sun at night.
There were only small silences
that seemed to grow
whenever she was around.

After the incident with her uncle's hut,
the whole village gathered.
Shuffling their feet in the grey drifts of ash
they asked her kindly to leave.
So there she is,
living up the mountain.

At night, just able to see
the flickering light of her fire,
the villagers huddle for warmth, pretending
not to feel something is missing.

ME & YOU

The long-legged girl who takes goal-kicks
is me.
I loop my j's and g's,
twiddle my hair
and wobble a loose tooth
through History yesterday afternoon.

The small shy boy who draws dragons
is you.
You understand mathematics,
make delicious cheese scones
and when my tooth finally falls out
and I cry in surprise,
you hand me a crumpled tissue.

I will be an Olympic athlete;
win two silver medals.
You will be a vet
in whose gentle hands
cats purr and budgies speak.

We don't know this yet
but we will be each other's first date.
One kiss.
That's all . . . but
for the rest of our lives we will never forget.

In the meantime,
my tongue explores a toothless gap
and you lean over your desk and concentrate
on drawing the feathery, feathery
lines of a dragon's wing.

CLOUD THAT FELL

She feels the lively tug of us
through the string of a yellow kite.
Iced by night and scorched
by dawn she's weary
of thunder and zigzag light.

Drawn to the touch
of cows and grass
she spills like sky-milk through the trees.
Pouring down hills and over the fields,
she dulls the glitter of rivers and seas.

Snagged by a steeple,
she swallows our town,
muffling the bell and our fearful calls.
As she gathers the lost in her white arms,
each droplet of her
swirls and falls.

MUSIC'S PRAYER

You can rap or *do, ray, me* to me,
fill your night and day with me,
breathe out and float away with me
    — just don't forget to play me.

You can *far, so, la, ti, do* to me,
Lang Syne your Hogmanay to me,
LP, CD, DJ with me
    — just don't forget to play me.

You can hip-hop and hooray to me,
je suis désolé to me,
sing and clap and pray with me
    — just don't forget to play me.

You can jazz, blues or ballet to me,
desert island castaway with me,
shut your eyes and sway to me
    — just don't forget to play me.

THE CANCAN

When I dance
my blood runs like a river can,
my feet fly like the birds can,
my heart beats like a drum can.
Because when I dance I can,
can do anything
when I dance.

Flying over rooftops
I see my town below me
where everybody knows me,
where all my problems throw me,
where heavy feet can slow me.
But nobody can, can stop me
when I dance.

My blood runs a race.
My feet fly in space.
My heart beats the pace.
Because when I dance I can,
can do anything
when I dance.

EXTINCT

We live only in books and photographs,
our stories all begin with 'Once',
three, two, going, going . . . gone.

Barbary Lion, Atitlan Grebe,
Caribbean Monk Seal, Carolina Parakeet.

We tasted good, our forests were yours
Our horn was valuable, you wore our furs,
three, two, going, going . . . gone.

Laughing Owl, Passenger Pigeon,
Javan Tiger, Japanese Sea Lion.

We flew and swam beneath the sun,
nested, hunted, raised our young,
three, two, going, going . . . gone.

Western Black Rhinoceros, Aldabra Snail,
Pyrenean Ibex, Wake Island Rail

Shells, tails, whiskers and bone,
three, two, going, going . . .

SMILE

If your smile
were a swing it would seat two people
leaning back and swooping
into the whooping sky.

If your smile
were a hammock I could lie in it and sleep,
the curve of me suspended
in the sweetest of dreams.

If your smile
were a rope we would skip on rhymes:
I like coffee, I like tea,
I'd like you to jump with me!

Half-moon smile
that vanishes fears.

Banana-wide smile
that makes bumps heal.

Sunshine smile
that dries my tears.

LOST IT, FOUND IT

I looked inside a pocket
I looked beneath a garden rock
I looked into an elephant's eye
I looked in a flower pot

I looked on the top of a double-decker bus
I looked in a second-hand shop
I looked past the red of a rainbow
I looked inside a book

I looked on the top of a mountain
I looked down the bottom of a well
I looked in the toe of a wellington boot
I looked inside a shell

I looked in the pouch of a kangaroo
I looked into the sea
I looked up a redbrick chimney
I looked in a hole in a tree

I looked in sunlight, I looked in rain
I looked in a lift, I looked on a train
I looked in the chorus of a song
Guess where I found it?

Here! It was right here all along

DREAM FEAST

Pepper and salt season my sleep,
there's a busy kitchen in my head
dishing up dreams.

Its cook wanders busy markets
picking out a sprig of thyme,
a measure of flour and honey.

This cook is wise; clues
are iced onto cakes,
secrets are hidden in pies.

I grip my knife and fork,
tuck a serviette into my nightie
and close my eyes.

NIGHT NIGHT

Up those dancers dearest,
climb the wooden hill.
Dreams await down Sheet Lane,
the sun is setting still.

Hike the zigzag path,
the moon is rising higher.
Take those gallopers two at a time
up to Bedfordshire.

Jump the Sleepytown Express
up those apples and pears.
Snug as a bug in a rug you'll be
when you get to Blanket Fair.